# PQA

## Preschool Program Quality Assessment

**Second Edition**

# Form B
# Agency Items
# Sections V–VII

HIGHSCOPE
PRESS ®

Ypsilanti, Michigan

Published by HighScope® Press
A division of the
HighScope Educational Research Foundation
600 North River Street
Ypsilanti, Michigan 48198-2898
Phone: 734-485-2000, FAX: 734-485-0704
E-mail: *info@highscope.org*
Web site: *www.highscope.org*

ISBN 978-1-57379-137-3

Printed in the United States of America
10 9 8 7 6 5 4 3 2 1

# CONTENTS

# PRESCHOOL PROGRAM QUALITY ASSESSMENT (PQA)
## FORM B: AGENCY ITEMS (SECTIONS V–VII)
## PROGRAM/RATER INFORMATION

## I. PROGRAM INFORMATION

Name of agency

Name of center/site

Name of classroom being observed

### Program director/administrator or contact person

Name

Position/Title

Telephone (          )                    Ext.          Fax

E-mail

## II. RATER INFORMATION

Name

Agency

Position/title

Telephone (          )                    Ext.          Fax

E-mail

## III. PRESCHOOL PQA ADMINISTRATION INFORMATION

Date/time interview began

Date/time interview ended

**Comments or notes about administering the Preschool PQA at this site:**

Rater's signature                                        Date

# PRESCHOOL PQA ITEMS

## Classroom Items (Form A)

**I. LEARNING ENVIRONMENT**
- A. Safe and healthy environment
- B. Defined interest areas
- C. Logically located interest areas
- D. Outdoor space, equipment, materials
- E. Organization and labeling of materials
- F. Varied and open-ended materials
- G. Plentiful materials
- H. Diversity-related materials
- I. Displays of child-initiated work

**II. DAILY ROUTINE**
- A. Consistent daily routine
- B. Parts of the day
- C. Appropriate time for each part of day
- D. Time for child planning
- E. Time for child-initiated activities
- F. Time for child recall
- G. Small-group time
- H. Large-group time
- I. Choices during transition times
- J. Cleanup time with reasonable choices
- K. Snack or meal time
- L. Outside time

**III. ADULT-CHILD INTERACTION**
- A. Meeting basic physical needs
- B. Handling separation from home
- C. Warm and caring atmosphere
- D. Support for child communication
- E. Support for non-English speakers
- F. Adults as partners in play
- G. Encouragement of child initiatives
- H. Support for child learning at group times
- I. Opportunities for child exploration
- J. Acknowledgment of child efforts
- K. Encouragement for peer interactions
- L. Independent problem solving
- M. Conflict resolution

**IV. CURRICULUM PLANNING AND ASSESSMENT**
- A. Curriculum model
- B. Team teaching
- C. Comprehensive child records
- D. Anecdotal note taking by staff
- E. Use of child observation measure

## Agency Items (Form B)

**V. PARENT INVOLVEMENT AND FAMILY SERVICES**
- A. Opportunities for involvement
- B. Parents on policy-making committees
- C. Parent participation in child activities
- D. Sharing of curriculum information
- E. Staff-parent informal interactions
- F. Extending learning at home
- G. Formal meetings with parents
- H. Diagnostic/special education services
- I. Service referrals as needed
- J. Transition to kindergarten

**VI. STAFF QUALIFICATIONS AND STAFF DEVELOPMENT**
- A. Program director background
- B. Instructional staff background
- C. Support staff orientation and supervision
- D. Ongoing professional development
- E. Inservice training content and methods
- F. Observation and feedback
- G. Professional organization affiliation

**VII. PROGRAM MANAGEMENT**
- A. Program licensed
- B. Continuity in instructional staff
- C. Program assessment
- D. Recruitment and enrollment plan
- E. Operating policies and procedures
- F. Accessibility for those with disabilities
- G. Adequacy of program funding

# SCORING INSTRUCTIONS

## Step 1

**Conduct interview with the program director or other knowledgeable staff members. Record supporting evidence in the spaces provided in each row of boxes.**

What you see, hear, and write down provides the evidence for the level of quality you select in step 3. Use the standard questions, which appear above the indicators, to elicit information. Supporting evidence for the indicator level you choose includes any of the following, as needed, for each item:

• Anecdotes: brief notes on what children and/or staff actually do and/or communicate

• Quotes: what children and/or staff actually say

• Materials lists

• Diagrams of the room, space, area, and/or outdoor play yard; sketches and notations

• Sequences of daily events and routines

• Answers to questions (see specific wording of questions under relevant items)

## Step 2

**Read each row of indicators. Check one box per row.**

Once you have gathered supporting evidence for an item, read the rows of indicators that follow it. Based on the evidence you have gathered in Step 1, place a checkmark (✓) in *one and only one* box (1, 3, or 5) of each row of indicators. *Try to complete every row for every item.* If a row of boxes does not apply (for example, if it is a half-day program without naptime), make a note to that effect next to the row and do not check any boxes in that row.

## Step 3

**Determine the quality level. Circle the corresponding level at the top of the form: 1, 2, 3, 4, or 5.**

Determine the quality level for the item using the following criteria:

*For items with **three or more rows** of boxes*

    Level 1: Half or more of the level 1 boxes are checked (regardless of the level 3 or level 5 boxes that may be checked).

    Level 2: Fewer than half of the level 1 boxes are checked, and some of the level 3 and/or level 5 boxes are checked.

    Level 3: Half or more of the level 3 boxes are checked, and no level 1 boxes are checked.

    Level 4: Fewer than half of the level 3 boxes are checked, and the remaining boxes are checked at level 5.

    Level 5: All the level 5 boxes are checked, and no level 1 boxes or level 3 boxes are checked.

*For items with **two rows** of boxes*

    Level 1: Both level 1 boxes are checked.

    Level 2: One level 1 box and either one level 3 box or one level 5 box are checked.

    Level 3: Both level 3 boxes are checked.

    Level 4: One level 3 box and one level 5 box are checked.

    Level 5: Both level 5 boxes are checked.

If a row of boxes is "not applicable" or cannot be observed or determined by interview, compute the quality level based on the number of rows that are completed for that item. If and only if no rows are completed in the item, check "Not observed or reported" and enter "NR" on the Summary Sheet.

*For additional instructions on administering the Preschool PQA, see the **Preschool PQA Administration Manual**.*

Training results in the most effective use of the Preschool PQA. To arrange Preschool PQA training for staff members or independent raters who will be completing this instrument, please contact the Training Coordinator, High/Scope Educational Research Foundation, 600 North River Street, Ypsilanti, MI 48198-2898; Phone: 1-734-485-2000, ext. 218; FAX: 1-734-485-4467; E-Mail: *training@highscope.org*. Or visit the High/Scope Web site—*www.highscope.org*—for more information on training programs or to register online.

# V. PARENT INVOLVEMENT AND FAMILY SERVICES

**V–A. The program provides a variety of opportunities for parents to become involved in the program.**

*Circle one indicator level for this item based on the scoring rules on page 4.*

**1    2    3    4    5**

☐ **Check here if not observed or reported.**

*Standard Questions*
1. Are parents informed about and involved in program activities? (If yes) How?
2. Does the program encourage parent participation? (If yes) How?

| Level 1 Indicators | Level 3 Indicators | Level 5 Indicators | Supporting Evidence/Anecdotes |
|---|---|---|---|
| ☐ There are no activities or materials to help parents become involved in the program. | ☐ The program provides some parent-oriented activities or materials to help parents become involved in the program. | ☐ There are many parent involvement options consistent with a variety of parent interests and time constraints, e.g., parents may<br>• Volunteer in the classroom<br>• Bring in materials<br>• Attend parent meetings and workshops<br>• Serve on parent advisory councils<br>• Meet with teachers to discuss children's progress<br>• Support children's learning at home<br>• Read or contribute to a parent newsletter | |
| ☐ The program does not encourage parent participation. | ☐ The program sometimes encourages parent participation. | ☐ The program encourages parent participation (e.g., providing child care, arranging transportation, scheduling events at times convenient for parents, making reminder phone calls the day before, networking parents with one another). | |

# V. PARENT INVOLVEMENT AND FAMILY SERVICES

*Circle **one** indicator level for this item based on the scoring rules on page 4.*

## V–B. Parents are represented on program advisory and/or policymaking committees.

1    2    3    4    5

☐ **Check here if not observed or reported.**

*Standard Questions*

1. Does the program have an advisory council or other policymaking group? (If yes):
   a. Who is on the council/committee?
   b. How often does it meet?
   c. What role(s) do the members play?

| Level 1 Indicators | Level 3 Indicators | Level 5 Indicators | Supporting Evidence/Anecdotes |
|---|---|---|---|
| ☐ There are no program advisory or policymaking committees. | ☐ Program advisory or policymaking committee(s) exist but do not meet regularly. | ☐ Program advisory or policy committee(s) exist and meet according to a regular schedule. | |
| ☐ Parents are not represented on program advisory or policymaking committees. | ☐ Parents have some representation on program advisory or policymaking committee(s). | ☐ Parents have full representation on program advisory and policymaking committee(s). | |
| ☐ Parents have no voice in program policies. | ☐ Parents sometimes speak up or vote on program policies. | ☐ Parents attend meetings and have a say in establishing program policies. | |

# V. PARENT INVOLVEMENT AND FAMILY SERVICES

Circle **one** indicator level for this item based on the scoring rules on page 4.

## V–C. Parents are encouraged to participate in program activities with children.

1     2     3     4     5

☐ Check here if not observed or reported.

*Standard Questions*
1. Do you encourage parents to participate in children's program activities? (If yes) How?
2. Do you inform parents about children's program activities? (If yes) How?

| Level 1 Indicators | Level 3 Indicators | Level 5 Indicators | Supporting Evidence/Anecdotes |
|---|---|---|---|
| ☐ Parents are not encouraged to volunteer in the classroom, go on field trips, or participate in other activities with children (e.g., parents not allowed beyond a certain point when they drop off or pick up children; no sign-up list for parents to volunteer). | ☐ Parents are sometimes invited or encouraged to participate in some activities with children (e.g., parents volunteer in the classroom but perform primarily custodial roles). | ☐ Parents are often invited or encouraged to participate in a variety of activities with children (e.g., parents volunteer in the classroom and play an active role in the day's activities, special events, and field trips; parents bring in recyclables and help to make play materials). | |
| ☐ Program staff tend to avoid or ignore family members when they ask about children's program activities. | ☐ Program staff respond positively to questions from family members about children's program activities. | ☐ Program staff seek out and approach family members to initiate conversations about children's program activities. | |

# V. PARENT INVOLVEMENT AND FAMILY SERVICES

**V–D. Staff and parents exchange information about the curriculum and its relationship to children's development.**

☐ **Check here if not observed or reported.**

*Standard Questions*

1. Do you inform parents about the curriculum and its relationship to children's development?
   (If yes) How?
2. Do parents provide input about the curriculum and its relationship to children's development?
   (If yes) How?

| Level 1 Indicators | Level 3 Indicators | Level 5 Indicators | Supporting Evidence/Anecdotes |
|---|---|---|---|
| ☐ Staff and parents do not exchange information about the curriculum and its relationship to children's development. | ☐ Staff provide parents with information about the curriculum and its relationship to children's development (e.g., an information packet is given or mailed to parents; staff tell parents how the program works). | ☐ Staff and parents exchange information about the curriculum and its relationship to children's development (e.g., staff send regular mailings or newsletters about the program and invite parent reactions; staff and parents interact during program workshops; staff and parents exchange frequent informal comments about activities; staff invite observations and answer questions from parents about the program). | |
| ☐ Staff do not seek input from parents about the program and its relationship to children's development. | ☐ Staff sometimes seek input from parents about the program and its relationship to children's development. | ☐ Staff seek input from parents about the program and its relationship to children's development. | |

# V. PARENT INVOLVEMENT AND FAMILY SERVICES

*Circle **one** indicator level for this item based on the scoring rules on page 4.*

**V-E. Staff and parents interact informally to share information about the day's activities and children's experiences.**

1   2   3   4   5

☐ **Check here if not observed or reported.**

*Standard Questions*

1. Do you interact informally with parents about their children's daily experiences? (If yes):
   a. How?
   b. How often?

| **Level 1 Indicators** | **Level 3 Indicators** | **Level 5 Indicators** | **Supporting Evidence/Anecdotes** |
|---|---|---|---|
| ☐ Staff and parents do not interact informally. | ☐ Staff and parents sometimes interact informally. | ☐ Staff and parents frequently interact informally to update each other about the child's recent experiences (e.g., conversing during drop-off and pick-up times, bringing in or sending home things the child has made, sending notes, making calls). | |
| ☐ Staff communicate with parents in a blunt, distracted, or disinterested manner. | ☐ Staff communicate respectfully with parents. | ☐ Staff use an interested and unhurried manner to communicate clearly, honestly, and respectfully with parents about the program, their children, and issues of interest or concern. | |

# V. PARENT INVOLVEMENT AND FAMILY SERVICES

*Circle **one** indicator level for this item based on the scoring rules on page 4.*

**V–F. Staff and parents exchange information about how to promote and extend children's learning and social development at home.**

I    2    3    4    5

☐ **Check here if not observed or reported.**

*Standard Question*

1. Do you exchange information with parents about supporting children's learning at home?
   (If yes) How?

| Level 1 Indicators | Level 3 Indicators | Level 5 Indicators | Supporting Evidence/Anecdotes |
|---|---|---|---|
| ☐ Staff and parents do not exchange ideas or materials to support children's learning and social development at home. | ☐ Staff and parents exchange some ideas or materials to support children's learning and social development at home. | ☐ Staff and parents exchange many ideas and materials to support children's learning and social development at home (e.g., ideas and materials might pertain to the educational potential of ordinary household objects, how everyday family activities can be social learning experiences, how to promote language development). | |
| ☐ Staff do not seek input from parents about how they are supporting children's development at home. | ☐ Staff sometimes seek input from parents about how they are supporting children's development at home. | ☐ Staff seek input from parents about how they are supporting children's development at home and provide parents with additional resources. | |

# V. PARENT INVOLVEMENT AND FAMILY SERVICES

*Circle **one** indicator level for this item based on the scoring rules on page 4.*

**V–G. Staff members schedule home visits and formal parent conferences to share information with parents and seek input from parents about the program and their children's development.**
[Note: Do not count meetings that are specially called by teachers or parents because of problems in the program.]

1     2     3     4     5

☐ **Check here if not observed or reported.**

*Standard Questions*
1. Do you schedule home visits? (If yes):
   a. How often?
   b. What happens during home visits?
2. Do you schedule parent-teacher conferences? (If yes):
   a. How often?
   b. What happens during conferences?

| Level 1 Indicators | Level 3 Indicators | Level 5 Indicators | Supporting Evidence/Anecdotes |
|---|---|---|---|
| ☐ Staff do not conduct home visits. | ☐ Staff conduct home visits as needed. | ☐ Staff conduct home visits for every child and family. | |
| ☐ Staff do not schedule conferences with each child's parent/guardian. | ☐ Staff schedule one conference per year with each child's parent/guardian. | ☐ Staff schedule two or more conferences per year with each child's parent/guardian. | |
| ☐ Staff do not use visits/conferences to share information about the program and children's development. | ☐ Staff use visits/conferences to share information about the program and children's development. | ☐ Staff use visits/conferences to share information and seek input from parents about the program and children's development. | |

# V. PARENT INVOLVEMENT AND FAMILY SERVICES

Circle **one** indicator level for this item based on the scoring rules on page 4.

**V-H. The program or its host agency provides diagnostic and special education services for special needs children.**

1    2    3    4    5

☐ **Check here if not observed or reported.**

[Note: Services may be provided directly or through referrals to other community agencies.]

*Standard Questions*

1. Does the program provide diagnostic and/or special education services for children? (If yes):
   a. What services?
   b. How are the services provided?
2. Does the program provide referrals for diagnostic and/or special education services for children? (If yes):
   a. What referrals?
   b. How are the referrals made?

| Level 1 Indicators | Level 3 Indicators | Level 5 Indicators | Supporting Evidence/Anecdotes |
|---|---|---|---|
| ☐ Children are neither provided with nor referred for diagnostic and special education services. | ☐ Children are provided with/referred for diagnostic and special education services in some areas of development. | ☐ Children are provided with/referred for diagnostic and/or special education services as needed for suspected or diagnosed disabilities in speech, language, physical, visual, audiological, and social development (and in other areas as needed). | |
| ☐ Staff do not provide parents with information to locate or access special education services needed by the child. | ☐ Staff give parents information for parents to locate and access special education services needed by the child. | ☐ Staff work together with parents to locate and access any special education services needed by the child. | |

# V. PARENT INVOLVEMENT AND FAMILY SERVICES

**V-I. Staff provide parents with referrals and access to supportive services as needed.**

Circle **one** indicator level for this item based on the scoring rules on page 4.

1    2    3    4    5

☐ **Check here if not observed or reported.**

*Standard Questions*

1. How familiar are you (or someone else on staff) with the needs of families and community resources related to these needs? For example, would you say "not familiar," "somewhat familiar," or "very familiar"?

2. Do you (or does someone else on staff) refer families for services or help them access services? (If yes) How are referrals or access to services handled?

| Level 1 Indicators | Level 3 Indicators | Level 5 Indicators | Supporting Evidence/Anecdotes |
|---|---|---|---|
| ☐ Staff are not aware of family needs. | ☐ Staff have some knowledge of family needs. | ☐ Staff are familiar with family needs (e.g., staff conduct or have access to needs assessments, intake interviews, or other information-gathering activities with families). | |
| ☐ Staff are not aware of available community resources. | ☐ Staff have some knowledge of community resources. | ☐ Staff are familiar with resources available in the community (e.g., staff maintain a library of services and referral procedures; staff attend community service workshops). | |
| ☐ Staff do not make referrals to needed family services. | ☐ Staff sometimes make referrals to needed family services. | ☐ Staff make referrals to needed family services (e.g., brochures and other information are readily available to parents; staff keep lists of local service providers). | |
| ☐ Staff do not facilitate access to family services. | ☐ Staff sometimes facilitate access to family services. | ☐ Staff facilitate access to family services (e.g., staff provide documentation for parents to share with providers; staff make initial phone call to help arrange appointment; staff help families find child care or transportation so they can use community resources). | |

# V. PARENT INVOLVEMENT AND FAMILY SERVICES

**V-J. Program activities are coordinated with community agencies and/or the public schools to facilitate the delivery of services to families and/or children's transition to kindergarten.**

*Circle **one** indicator level for this item based on the scoring rules on page 4.*

### 1    2    3    4    5

☐ **Check here if not observed or reported.**

*Standard Questions*

1. Are program activities coordinated with community agencies and/or the public schools to facilitate service delivery and/or children's transition to kindergarten? (If yes) How?
2. Are parents involved in the coordination and/or transition? (If yes) How?

| Level 1 Indicators | Level 3 Indicators | Level 5 Indicators | Supporting Evidence/Anecdotes |
|---|---|---|---|
| ☐ Program activities are not coordinated with community agencies and/or the public schools. | ☐ Program activities are sometimes coordinated with community agencies and/or the public schools. | ☐ Program activities are regularly coordinated with community agencies and/or the public schools (e.g., by mutual referrals, telephone and written contacts, staff participation on community advisory boards, exchanges of information about program goals and activities). | |
| ☐ Staff do not involve parents in program activities with community agencies and/or public schools. | ☐ Staff sometimes involve parents in program activities with community agencies and/or public schools. | ☐ Staff and parents work together to coordinate program activities with community agencies and/or public schools (e.g., staff provide parents with anecdotal notes or other records to share with kindergarten teachers and service providers). | |

# VI. STAFF QUALIFICATIONS AND STAFF DEVELOPMENT

## VI-A. The program director has the appropriate education, training, and experience.

*Circle **one** indicator level for this item based on the scoring rules on page 4.*

**1  2  3  4  5**

☐ **Check here if not observed or reported.**

Standard Questions

1. Please describe your education, training, and experience. For example:
   a. Do you have a degree? (If yes) In what?
   b. Have you taken courses or attended other training in child development and/or early childhood education? (If yes) What courses/training?
   c. What relevant work experiences have you had, for example, working with young children and families? Supervising early childhood staff? Evaluating early childhood programs? Managing early childhood programs?

| Level 1 Indicators | Level 3 Indicators | Level 5 Indicators | Supporting Evidence/Anecdotes |
|---|---|---|---|
| ☐ The program director does not have a bachelor's degree in early childhood education or child development. | ☐ The program director has a bachelor's degree in early childhood education or child development. | ☐ The program director has a graduate degree in early childhood education or child development. | |
| ☐ The program director does not have course work or training in a field relevant to early childhood education or child development. | ☐ The program director has some additional course work or training in related fields. | ☐ The program director has additional course work or training in related fields, such as<br>• Curriculum development<br>• Program evaluation<br>• Program management<br>• Staff development | |
| ☐ The program director has one year or less of relevant job experience. | ☐ The program director has 2–4 years of relevant job experience. | ☐ The program director has 5 or more years of relevant job experience that includes<br>• Working with young children in a group setting<br>• Program planning and implementation<br>• Program evaluation<br>• Staff supervision and development<br>• Program management | |

# VI. STAFF QUALIFICATIONS AND STAFF DEVELOPMENT

**VI-B. Instructional staff have the appropriate education, training, and experience.**

*Circle **one** indicator level for this item based on the scoring rules on page 4.*

|   |   |   |   |   |
|---|---|---|---|---|
| **1** | **2** | **3** | **4** | **5** |

☐ Check here if not observed or reported.

*Standard Questions*

1. Please describe the education and training of your teachers. Do they have degrees or credentials? (If yes) In what field(s)?
2. Please describe the education and training of your assistant teachers and aides. Do they have degrees or credentials? (If yes) In what field(s)?
3. How many years of early childhood experience does each of your head/lead teachers have?

| Level 1 Indicators | Level 3 Indicators | Level 5 Indicators | Supporting Evidence/Anecdotes |
|---|---|---|---|
| ☐ Fewer than half of the teachers have the appropriate education. | ☐ Half or more of the teachers have the appropriate education. | ☐ All the teachers have a bachelor's degree or higher in early childhood education, child development, or a related field. | |
| ☐ Fewer than half of the assistants, aides, or paraprofessionals have the appropriate education. | ☐ Half or more of the assistants, aides, or paraprofessionals have the appropriate education. | ☐ All the assistants, aides, and paraprofessionals have an associate's degree, CDA, or comparable early childhood certification. | |
| ☐ Head/lead teachers average one year or less of relevant job experience. | ☐ Head/lead teachers average 2–4 years of relevant job experience. | ☐ Head/lead teachers average 5 or more years of relevant job experience with young children including<br>• Program planning and implementation<br>• Child observation and evaluation<br>• Mentoring other staff | |

16

# VI. STAFF QUALIFICATIONS AND STAFF DEVELOPMENT

*Circle one indicator level for this item based on the scoring rules on page 4.*

**1    2    3    4    5**

☐ **Check here if not observed or reported.**

## VI-C. Support staff (e.g., cook, bus driver, secretary) and volunteers receive the appropriate orientation and supervision.

*Standard Questions*

1. Do you screen support staff? (If yes) How?
2. How do you decide what duties to assign support staff?
3. Do support staff and volunteers receive any orientation and training? (If yes) What?
4. Do you supervise support staff and volunteers? (If yes) How?

| Level 1 Indicators | Level 3 Indicators | Level 5 Indicators | Supporting Evidence/Anecdotes |
|---|---|---|---|
| ☐ Support staff are not screened. | ☐ Support staff are sometimes screened. | ☐ Support staff are screened with background checks and interviews. | |
| ☐ Support staff are not assigned duties appropriate to their background and skills. | ☐ Support staff are sometimes assigned duties appropriate to their background and skills. | ☐ Support staff are assigned duties appropriate to their background and skills. | |
| ☐ Support staff and volunteers are not oriented and trained in program procedures relevant to their roles. | ☐ Support staff and volunteers are sometimes oriented and trained in program procedures relevant to their roles. | ☐ Support staff and volunteers are oriented and trained in program procedures relevant to their roles. | |
| ☐ Support staff and volunteers do not receive ongoing supervision. | ☐ Support staff and volunteers sometimes receive ongoing supervision. | ☐ Support staff and volunteers receive ongoing supervision. | |

**SCHOOL OF EDUCATION
CURRICULUM LABORATORY
UM-DEARBORN**

# VI. STAFF QUALIFICATIONS AND STAFF DEVELOPMENT

*Circle **one** indicator level for this item based on the scoring rules on page 4.*

**1     2     3     4     5**

☐ **Check here if not observed or reported.**

**VI-D. Staff participate in ongoing professional development activities such as conferences, workshops, college-level courses and seminars, compiling or consulting a resource library, teacher exchanges, observation, mentoring, and coaching.**

*Standard Questions*

1. Do teachers participate in professional development activities? (If yes):
   a. What activities?
   b. How many participate?
   c. How many times per year?
2. Do you participate in professional development activities? (If yes):
   a. What activities?
   b. How many times per year?
3. Do support staff participate in professional development activities? (If yes):
   a. What activities?
   b. How many participate?
   c. How many times per year?

| Level 1 Indicators | Level 3 Indicators | Level 5 Indicators | Supporting Evidence/Anecdotes |
|---|---|---|---|
| ☐ Teachers do not participate in professional development activities. | ☐ Some or all teachers participate in 1–4 professional development activities per year. | ☐ All teachers participate in 5 or more professional development activities per year. | |
| ☐ Director(s) do not participate in professional development activities. | ☐ Director(s) participate in 1–4 professional development activities per year. | ☐ Director(s) participate in 5 or more professional development activities per year. | |
| ☐ Support staff do not participate in professional development activities. | ☐ Some or all support staff participate in 1–4 professional development activities per year. | ☐ All support staff participate in 5 or more professional development activities per year. | |

# VI. STAFF QUALIFICATIONS AND STAFF DEVELOPMENT

**VI-E. Inservice training sessions are specific to early childhood and apply the principles of adult learning.**
[Note: If Indicator Level I is checked in the first row, "Inservice training session(s) are not offered," do not complete the other rows. Score the entire item as "1."]

☐ **Check here if not observed or reported.**

*Standard Questions*

1. Does the agency offer inservice training? (If yes):
   a. How many sessions per year?
   b. What topic(s) does it cover?
   c. Is it based on one or more curriculum model(s)? (If one) Does the model provide theory? practice?
   d. Who provides training? What is the relationship of staff to the trainer(s)?
   e. How would you characterize training sessions. For example, are they lectures? Do they involve hands-on activities, discussion, practice?
   f. Do staff reflect on and share their training and practice experiences? (If yes) How?

| Level 1 Indicators | Level 3 Indicators | Level 5 Indicators | Supporting Evidence/Anecdotes |
|---|---|---|---|
| ☐ Inservice training session(s) are not offered. | ☐ Inservice training session(s) are offered 1–4 times a year. | ☐ Inservice training sessions are offered 5 times a year or more. | |
| **If inservice training is offered** <br> ☐ Inservice training addresses topics unrelated to early childhood development and program practices (e.g., how to prepare a resume, making holiday decorations). | **If inservice training is offered** <br> ☐ Inservice training sometimes addresses topics specific to early childhood development and program practices. | **If inservice training is offered** <br> ☐ Inservice training consistently addresses topics specific to early childhood development and program practices (e.g., social development, promoting early literacy, small-group time). | |
| **If inservice training is offered** <br> ☐ Training is not based on a curriculum model. | **If inservice training is offered** <br> ☐ Training is based on more than one curriculum model. | **If inservice training is offered** <br> ☐ Training is based on a consistent curriculum model that integrates theory and practice. | |

*(Item VI-E continues on the next page.)*

| Level 1 Indicators | Level 3 Indicators | Level 5 Indicators | Supporting Evidence/Anecdotes |
|---|---|---|---|
| **If inservice training is offered**<br>☐ Staff do not have ongoing relationship(s) with the same trainer(s). | **If inservice training is offered**<br>☐ Staff sometimes have ongoing relationship(s) with the same trainer(s). | **If inservice training is offered**<br>☐ Staff have ongoing relationships with the same trainer(s) that provide continuity and build on staff's cumulative knowledge. | |
| **If inservice training is offered**<br>☐ Training sessions are primarily trainer-directed lectures. | **If inservice training is offered**<br>☐ Training sessions sometimes involve staff members actively. | **If inservice training is offered**<br>☐ Training sessions regularly involve staff members actively through hands-on workshops, group discussions, and practice activities. | |
| **If inservice training is offered**<br>☐ Staff do not reflect on what they are doing or share their experiences. | **If inservice training is offered**<br>☐ Staff occasionally reflect on what they are doing or share their experiences. | **If inservice training is offered**<br>☐ Staff regularly reflect on what they are doing and share their experiences. | |

# VI. STAFF QUALIFICATIONS AND STAFF DEVELOPMENT

*Circle **one** indicator level for this item based on the scoring rules on page 4.*

**1     2     3     4     5**

☐ **Check here if not observed or reported.**

## VI-F. Instructional staff are regularly observed in the program setting and provided with feedback by someone familiar with the curriculum's goals, objectives, and methods for working with children.

*Standard Questions*

1. Are instructional staff observed in the program and given feedback? (If yes) How often?
2. Is the person responsible for evaluating staff unfamiliar, moderately familiar, or very familiar with the curriculum?
3. Do staff participate in the evaluation process? (If yes) How?

| Level 1 Indicators | Level 3 Indicators | Level 5 Indicators | Supporting Evidence/Anecdotes |
|---|---|---|---|
| ☐ Instructional staff are not observed or given feedback. | ☐ Instructional staff are observed and given feedback 1–2 times per year. | ☐ Instructional staff are observed and given feedback 3 or more times per year. | |
| ☐ The person responsible for evaluating staff is not familiar with the curriculum. | ☐ The person responsible for evaluating staff is moderately familiar with the curriculum. | ☐ The person responsible for evaluating staff is very familiar with the curriculum. | |
| ☐ Staff do not participate in the evaluation process. | ☐ Staff sometimes participate in the evaluation process. | ☐ Staff participate as equals in the evaluation process and discuss ways to build on strengths and improve the quality of the program based on the curriculum. | |

# VI. STAFF QUALIFICATIONS AND STAFF DEVELOPMENT

**VI-G.** The director and teachers are affiliated with a local, state, and/or national early childhood professional organization.

*Circle **one** indicator level for this item based on the scoring rules on page 4.*

**1    2    3    4    5**

☐ Check here if not observed or reported.

*Standard Questions*

1. Are you a member of an early childhood professional organization? (If yes):
   a. How often do you attend meetings?
   b. Does the agency reimburse any of the costs of your membership or attendance at meetings?
2. Are your staff members of an early childhood professional organization? (If yes):
   a. How many are members?
   b. How often do they attend meetings?
   c. Does the agency reimburse any of the costs of their membership or attendance at meetings?

| Level 1 Indicators | Level 3 Indicators | Level 5 Indicators | Supporting Evidence/Anecdotes |
|---|---|---|---|
| ☐ The director and teachers are not members of an early childhood professional organization. | ☐ The director and some of the teachers are members of an early childhood professional organization. | ☐ The director and all of the teachers are members of an early childhood professional organization. | |
| ☐ The director and teachers do not attend meetings of an early childhood professional organization. | ☐ The director and teachers occasionally attend meetings of an early childhood professional organization. | ☐ The director and teachers regularly attend meetings of an early childhood professional organization. | |
| ☐ The agency does not reimburse any of the costs of membership or attendance at meetings. | ☐ The agency reimburses some of the costs of one membership or attendance at one meeting. | ☐ The agency reimburses all of the costs of at least one membership and attendance at one meeting. | |

# VII. PROGRAM MANAGEMENT

## VII-A. The program is licensed based on regulations passed by the state and/or local licensing agencies.

*Circle **one** indicator level for this item based on the scoring rules on page 4.*

1    2    3    4    5

☐ **Check here if not observed or reported.**

*Standard Questions*
1. Does your program have a license or a provisional license? (If no license or a provisional license):
   a. What licensing standards are not met by your program?
   b. Are you working on meeting these standards? (If yes) How?

| **Level 1 Indicators** | **Level 3 Indicators** | **Level 5 Indicators** | **Supporting Evidence/Anecdotes** |
|---|---|---|---|
| ☐ The program is not licensed. | ☐ The program is provisionally licensed. | ☐ The program is licensed. | |
| ☐ The program does not meet state and/or local standards. | ☐ The program meets some and/or is actively working on meeting state and/or local standards. | ☐ The program meets state and/or local standards for building codes, fire safety, health and sanitation, natural disasters and emergencies, and other policies and procedures to protect children, families, and staff. | |

23

# VII. PROGRAM MANAGEMENT

## VII-B. Program policies promote continuity of care by classroom adults (paid staff who work directly with children.)

*Circle **one** indicator level for this item based on the scoring rules on page 4.*

**1    2    3    4    5**

☐ **Check here if not observed or reported.**

*Standard Questions*
1. How many children are enrolled in the classroom(s) being observed?
2. How many enrolled children per adult are there in the classroom(s) being observed?
3. How many teaching staff are in the program? How many have left or been replaced in the past 12 months?

| Level 1 Indicators | Level 3 Indicators | Level 5 Indicators | Supporting Evidence/Anecdotes |
|---|---|---|---|
| ☐ Based on enrollment, there are 21 or more children per classroom. | ☐ Based on enrollment, there are 19–20 children per classroom. | ☐ Based on enrollment, there are 18 or fewer children per classroom. | |
| ☐ Based on enrollment, there are 11 or more children per classroom adult. | ☐ Based on enrollment, there are 10 children per classroom adult. | ☐ Based on enrollment, there are 9 or fewer children per classroom adult. | |
| ☐ Teacher turnover is high at 40% or more in the past 12 months. | ☐ Teacher turnover is moderate at 11%–39% in the past 12 months. | ☐ Teacher turnover is low at 10% or less in the past 12 months. | |

# VII. PROGRAM MANAGEMENT

## VII–C. Staff regularly conduct a program assessment and use the results to improve the program.

*Circle **one** indicator level for this item based on the scoring rules on page 4.*

**1    2    3    4    5**

☐ **Check here if not observed or reported.**

*Standard Questions*

1. Do staff assess the program? (If yes):
   a. How many times have they assessed the program within the last year?
   b. What aspects of the program have been assessed?
   c. How are the results of the program assessment used?

| Level 1 Indicators | Level 3 Indicators | Level 5 Indicators | Supporting Evidence/Anecdotes |
|---|---|---|---|
| ☐ Staff have not assessed the program within the last year. | ☐ Staff have assessed the program once within the last year. | ☐ Staff have assessed the program two or more times within the last year. | |
| ☐ Program assessment is not used to measure implementation. | ☐ Program assessment measures some aspects of implementation. | ☐ Program assessment measures all aspects of implementation including<br>• Classroom practices<br>• Planning and evaluation procedures<br>• Parent involvement<br>• Administrative procedures | |
| ☐ There is no systematic procedure to build on strengths and improve the program. | ☐ Results of the assessment are sometimes used to build on strengths and improve the program. | ☐ Results of the assessment are systematically used to build on strengths and improve the program including<br>• Identifying inservice training needs<br>• Revising management practices<br>• Seeking additional resources | |

# VII. PROGRAM MANAGEMENT

*Circle **one** indicator level for this item based on the scoring rules on page 4.*

## VII–D. The program has a child recruitment and enrollment plan.

**1    2    3    4    5**

☐ **Check here if not observed or reported.**

*Standard Questions*

1. Do you have a plan for recruiting and enrolling children? (If yes):
   a. What does the plan cover?
   b. Is the plan written down or otherwise documented?
2. Do parents receive enrollment materials? (If yes) What materials?
3. Do parents and children spend time in the program before the child's first day? (If yes):
   a. How much time?
   b. What do they do during this time?
4. Are there non–English-speaking families or parents/guardians with disabilities in your program? (If yes) How do you make program information materials available to them?

| Level 1 Indicators | Level 3 Indicators | Level 5 Indicators | Supporting Evidence/Anecdotes |
|---|---|---|---|
| ☐ The program has no child recruitment and enrollment plan. Children are recruited at random. | ☐ The program has a partially developed child recruitment and enrollment plan. | ☐ The program has a fully developed and documented child recruitment and enrollment plan that includes procedures for selection and placement. | |
| ☐ Parents do not receive enrollment materials. | ☐ Parents receive some enrollment materials. | ☐ Parents receive enrollment materials, including<br>• Program overview<br>• School calendar<br>• Information and permission forms<br>• School policies<br>• Payment schedule<br>• Enrollment procedures<br>• Withdrawal procedures | |
| ☐ Parents and children do not spend time at the program prior to the child's first day. | ☐ Parents and children spend 1 hour at the program prior to the child's first day. | ☐ Parents and children spend 2 or more hours at the program prior to the child's first day (e.g., observing, talking to teachers, meeting other parents and classmates, visiting and playing). | |

## Level 1 Indicators

**If Applicable***

☐ No effort is made to make program information available to persons who speak other languages or who have disabilities.

## Level 3 Indicators

**If Applicable***

☐ Limited efforts are made to make program information available to persons who speak other languages or who have disabilities.

## Level 5 Indicators

**If Applicable***

☐ A variety of efforts are made to make program information available to persons who speak other languages or who have disabilities (e.g., parent handbook translated or printed in large type).

## Supporting Evidence/Anecdotes

* **If Applicable:** If there are parents/guardians who do not speak English or have disabilities.

# VII. PROGRAM MANAGEMENT

**VII–E. The program has a fully developed set of operating policies and procedures.**

*Standard Questions*

1. For each of the following topics, does your agency have: an unwritten policy? a written policy? a procedure for implementing the policy consistently?
   a. Attendance
   b. Weather
   c. Illness
   d. Dispensing medication
   e. Discipline
   f. Accidents and emergencies
   g. Reporting child abuse and neglect
   h. Confidentiality
   i. Grievances

| Level 1 Indicators | Level 3 Indicators | Level 5 Indicators | Supporting Evidence/Anecdotes |
|---|---|---|---|
| ☐ There is no attendance policy. | ☐ There is an unwritten (informal) attendance policy. | ☐ There is a written attendance policy that is known by staff and parents and is consistently implemented. | |
| ☐ There is no weather policy. | ☐ There is an unwritten (informal) weather policy. | ☐ There is a written weather policy that is known by staff and parents and is consistently implemented. | |
| ☐ There is no illness policy. | ☐ There is an unwritten (informal) illness policy. | ☐ There is a written illness policy that is known by staff and parents and is consistently implemented. | |
| ☐ There is no medication policy. | ☐ There is an unwritten (informal) medication policy. | ☐ There is a written medication policy that is known by staff and parents and is consistently implemented. | |
| ☐ There is no discipline policy. | ☐ There is an unwritten (informal) discipline policy. | ☐ There is a written discipline policy that is known by staff and parents and is consistently implemented. | |

| Level 1 Indicators | Level 3 Indicators | Level 5 Indicators | Supporting Evidence/Anecdotes |
|---|---|---|---|
| ☐ There is no accident and emergency policy. | ☐ There is an unwritten (informal) accident and emergency policy. | ☐ There is a written accident and emergency policy that is known by staff and parents and is consistently implemented. | |
| ☐ There is no policy for reporting child abuse and neglect. | ☐ There is an unwritten (informal) policy for reporting child abuse and neglect. | ☐ There is a written policy for reporting child abuse and neglect that is known by staff and parents and is consistently implemented. | |
| ☐ There is no confidentiality policy. | ☐ There is an unwritten (informal) confidentiality policy. | ☐ There is a written confidentiality policy that is known by staff and parents and is consistently implemented. | |
| ☐ There is no grievance policy. | ☐ There is an unwritten (informal) grievance policy. | ☐ There is a written grievance policy that is known by staff and parents and is consistently implemented. | |

# VII. PROGRAM MANAGEMENT

## VII-F. The program is accessible to those with disabilities.

*Standard Questions*

1. Does your program have the following facilities to make it accessible to those with disabilities?
   a. Ramps
   b. Wide doors
   c. Accessible bathrooms and bathroom fixtures
   d. Accessible storage (shelves, hooks)
   e. Handicapped parking
2. (If yes to any/all of the above) Are these facilities well maintained?
3. (If no to any of the above) Are there plans to make these facilities available? (If yes) What?

| Level 1 Indicators | Level 3 Indicators | Level 5 Indicators | Supporting Evidence/Anecdotes |
|---|---|---|---|
| ☐ Program facilities are not barrier-free and accessible to persons with disabilities. | ☐ Some program facilities are barrier-free and accessible to persons with disabilities. | ☐ Program facilities are barrier-free and accessible to persons with disabilities. Features include <br> • Ramps <br> • Wide doors <br> • Accessible bathrooms <br> • Accessible storage (shelves, hooks) <br> • Handicapped parking | |
| ☐ There are no plans to make the facility barrier-free. | ☐ There are specific plans to make the facility barrier-free. | ☐ Barrier-free features are well maintained. | |

# VII. PROGRAM MANAGEMENT
## VII-G. The program is adequately funded.

*Circle **one** indicator level for this item based on the scoring rules on page 4.*

1   2   3   4   5

☐ **Check here if not observed or reported.**

*Standard Questions*

1. For each of the following, please describe whether your program is funded inadequately, partially, or fully:
   a. Keeping the classroom safe and well supplied with instructional equipment and materials
   b. Attracting and employing qualified staff at all levels, including salaries and benefits
   c. Covering staff development expenses, including workshop and conference fees, transportation, per diem, and substitute teacher costs
   d. Covering family involvement expenses including child care during meetings, materials and refreshments, and publication and distribution of manuals, newsletters, and other resources

| Level 1 Indicators | Level 3 Indicators | Level 5 Indicators | Supporting Evidence/Anecdotes |
|---|---|---|---|
| ☐ Funds are not adequate to correct unsafe conditions or to alleviate shortages of equipment and supplies. | ☐ Funds are adequate to provide for some but not all aspects of safety, equipment, and supplies. | ☐ Funds are adequate to keep the classroom safe and well supplied with instructional equipment and materials. | |
| ☐ Funds are not adequate to attract and employ qualified staff. | ☐ Funds are adequate to attract and employ qualified staff at some levels. | ☐ Funds are adequate to attract and employ qualified staff at all levels. Salaries and benefits match or exceed those at comparable agencies. | |
| ☐ Staff development funds are not adequate to pay authorized expenses for any staff. | ☐ Staff development funds are adequate to pay authorized expenses for some staff. | ☐ Staff development funds are adequate to pay authorized expenses for all staff including workshop and conference fees, transportation, per diem, and substitute teacher costs. | |
| ☐ Funds are not adequate to cover any of the expenses associated with parent involvement and family-oriented activities. | ☐ Funds are adequate to cover some of the expenses associated with parent involvement and family-oriented activities. | ☐ Funds are adequate to cover all of the expenses associated with parent involvement and family-oriented activities including child care during meetings, materials and refreshments, and publication and distribution of manuals, newsletters, and other resources. | |

Director's Name: _____

Rater's Name: _____

Program Name _____

Date of Assessment: _____

**Enter the numerical rating (1, 2, 3, 4, or 5) for each item. Refer to the Scoring Instructions on page 4. If an item was not rated, enter "NR."**

## V. PARENT INVOLVEMENT AND FAMILY SERVICES

____ A. Opportunities for involvement

____ B. Parents on policy-making committees

____ C. Parent participation in child activities

____ D. Sharing of curriculum information

____ E. Staff-parent informal interactions

____ F. Extending learning at home

____ G. Formal meetings with parents

____ H. Diagnostic/special education services

____ I. Service referrals as needed

____ J. Transition to kindergarten

## VII. PROGRAM MANAGEMENT

____ A. Program licensed

____ B. Continuity in instructional staff

____ C. Program assessment

____ D. Recruitment and enrollment plan

____ E. Operating policies and procedures

____ F. Accessibility for those with disabilities

____ G. Adequacy of program funding

## VI. STAFF QUALIFICATIONS AND STAFF DEVELOPMENT

____ A. Program director background

____ B. Instructional staff background

____ C. Support staff orientation and supervision

____ D. Ongoing professional development

____ E. Inservice training content and methods

____ F. Observation and feedback

____ G. Professional organization affiliation

____ NUMBER OF AGENCY ITEMS NOT RATED
(Number of items marked "NR")

____ NUMBER OF AGENCY ITEMS RATED
(24 minus the number not rated)

____ TOTAL AGENCY SCORE
(Sum of scores on rated items)

____ AVERAGE AGENCY SCORE
(Total score ÷ Number of items rated)